LFA Health Arts

T'ai Chi Si]

Movements 1 – 156

Explained in an easy to follow format

By Sheila Dickinson
President of the LFA Health Arts

Benefits:-
Helps to improve balance and co-ordination
Helps to improve joint mobility
Eases stress
Provides relaxation
Calms volatile emotions
Helps to find the circles and softness within our
movements.

Printed and published in Great Britain by

STAIRWAY
DISTRIBUTION
LTD.

P 0 BOX 19,
HEDON,
HULL
HU12 8YR

First Published 2002

Published by Stairway Distribution Limited
PO Box 19, Hedon. Hull. HU12 8YR
www.leefamilyarts.com

© Copyright Sheila Dickinson 2002
All rights reserved
ISBN 1-903711-04-5

Please consult your Doctor before taking part in the following exercise programme.
The LFA and Stairway Distribution Ltd disclaim any liability for loss or injury in connection with the advice and exercises included in this book.

Acknowledgements

To the past Masters of our Arts - we offer our sincere thanks!

Books by the same author:-

T'AI CHI FORM	(MOVEMENTS 1 TO 140)
T'AI CHI DANCE	(MOVEMENTS 1 TO 184)
T'AI CHI STICK	(MOVEMENTS 1 TO 150)
T'AI CHI SILK	(MOVEMENTS 1 TO 156)
T'AI CHI SWORD	(MOVEMENTS 1 TO 108)
T'AI CHI NUNCHAKU	(MOVEMENTS 1 TO 150)
T'AI CHI FAN	(MOVEMENTS 1 TO 150)

VIDEOS by the same author:-

T'AI CHI FORM	(MOVEMENTS 1 TO 50)
T'AI CHI DANCE	(MOVEMENTS 1 TO 50)
T'AI CHI STICK	(MOVEMENTS 1 TO 50)
T'AI CHI SILK	(MOVEMENTS 1 TO 50)
T'AI CHI SWORD	(MOVEMENTS 1 TO 50)

Available from: -

Stairway Distribution Limited
P O Box 19
Hedon
Hull
HU12 8YR
Tel / Fax 01482 896063

Or visit our Website www.leefamilyarts.com

THE LFA T'AI CHI LIBRARY

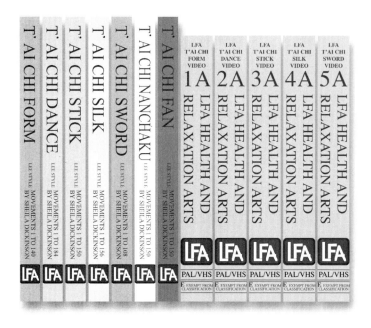

All of the above Books and Videos are available from:-
Stairway Distribution Limited
PO Box 19
Hedon
HU12 8YR
Tel/Fax 01482 896063

You may also order from our Website catalogue, please visit
www.leefamilyarts.com

CONTENTS

Foreword

My position as President of the Lee Family Arts started in January 1995. Since that time, I have had the privilege to guide my fellow instructors in all aspects of LFA T'ai Chi, and I have worked hard to reach as many people as possible, so that everyone may gain from the many health benefits of our Arts.

I would not be writing this book today without the guidance and patience of my late Grand Master Chee Soo, who spent most of his life teaching the Lee Family Arts. Chee Soo is in my thoughts constantly and I offer my sincere thanks for receiving the benefit of his wisdom and understanding.

Chee Soo wrote five books published by the Aquarian Press, sadly at the time of writing, only one title remains in print today 'The Chinese Art of T'ai Chi Ch'uan'. In this book he traces the history of the Lee Style back to Ho-Hsieh Lee circa 1,000BC. It is stated that the Lee Family have always been Taoists and that the Lee Style is a Yin and Yang style, this means that everything within it is in complete balance and harmony. Chee Soo occasionally spoke of his own Grand Master, Chan Kam Lee and told of how they had met during 1934 in Hyde Park in London. In those days there were very few Oriental people in

London and the two became friends. It was a friendship that would change Chee Soo's life forever. After Chan Kam Lee's death, Chee Soo dedicated himself to maintaining the knowledge and wisdom he had learnt from Chan Kam Lee.

While staying with my family and my self, Chee Soo talked to me about the future of the Lee Family Arts and the direction he wished them to take. On Monday the 16th May 1994 Chee Soo asked me to give him my word that I would not let the Lee Family Arts die.

Sadly Chee Soo died on the 29th August 1994.

It is with the greatest respect to Chee Soo that I offer my own writings and understanding of the lessons he taught me.

The names of Instructors who have trained, qualified and still maintain their own training can be obtained from the Lee Family Arts official register of qualified instructors. The LFA can only vouch for the quality and content of that which is taught within an official LFA registered class.

The Lee Family Arts have been tried and tested for thousands of years before we were born. The people who teach them are merely caretakers, who have the privilege of maintaining the Arts, and witnessing them helping others.

This book teaches you the complete one hundred and fifty six movements of the T'ai Chi Silk.
The Lee Family Arts will always be known as a Family Art and it is a family which grows in numbers daily. In concluding, I would like to say a very special welcome to you!

The Principles Of Good Health

Within the LFA, we believe we offer a valuable contribution towards good health:-

Mastering The Physical

People who show great physical strength or brute force, often lack physical energy. This is because large muscles tend to discourage the growth of your natural energy, creating tension, which in turn may restrict the flow of blood and create water retention. The knock on effect is that while some organs may swell in size, others may contract. This imbalance may well allow the full dynamic potential of your vitality to be run down, or lost.

My late Master Chee Soo stated in his book 'The Chinese Art of T'ai Chi Ch'uan' that anyone seriously interested in good health should try to adhere to the rules laid down by the early Taoists. These are called Ch'ang Ming (The Taoist Health Therapy for a Long Healthy Life).

The next recommended step is to learn the true meaning of correct weight distribution and balance. This can be discovered by practising the stances uses in our form sets i.e. T'ai Chi Form, Dance, Stick, Silk, Sword, Nunchaku and Fan. In our classes, students first learn the correct positions and weight distribution with their eyes open. When they have gained confidence by practising in this manner, the next stage is for them to practise the same positions and weight distribution with their eyes closed. This level may feel a little difficult at first, but it is an excellent way to feel what is really going on when you move from one position to the next.

Only when you feel comfortable with the stances should you move on. Next, we try and harmonise the stances, posture and technique. When you have mastered a few movements, close your eyes once again and try and feel more. If you practise only a few of our movements each day, you will eventually be able to reach a greater depth of understanding.

It is important to remember never to become too absorbed with the physical, although it is important to make sure you are in the correct positions. LFA T'ai Chi directs you to so much more than the physical.

Within the Lee Family Arts, it is taught that the parts of the body are complimentary to each other, in other words it is the top that exercises the bottom, while at the same time the bottom exercises the top. The right exercises the left and the left exercises the right. By practising our Arts you will learn to understand your own body in ways which you never thought possible. In Chee Soo's book 'The Taoist Ways Of Healing' it is written that once you attain the true good health of your own body, your physical energy will be able to fight all bacteria and viruses.

Mastering The Mind

This is a subject which has filled the pages of many books. From the beginning of your training you will find that your mind is given tasks to complete. People sometimes come to our classes suffering from stress, in my experience the worst thing you can say to a person suffering from stress is 'relax'. The LFA approach stress from an entirely different angle i.e. you are pleasantly occupied thinking about what to do with your hands and feet, that you do not have time to think about your personal worries. Before you know where you are, the class is over and you feel great.

We will teach you how to calm your mind without it being empty, so that you take control. Often the act of trying to empty the mind creates the opposite effect and we find ourselves back where we started.

T'ai Chi is sometimes known as meditation in motion. By regular practice, the time will come when the movements become second nature to you and you will find your mind totally relaxed. This result occurs quite naturally along the route of LFA T'ai Chi.

Many different aspects of mental control are taught

within our classes and on our day courses. They are not forced, everyone progresses at their own pace. In this world, every person is as important as the next, and it is important not to apply pressure to yourself or to be pressured. An expression which I often use in my classes is 'The only qualification you need to practise LFA T'ai Chi is to be able to smile'.

The Importance Of Breath

You will find that I talk constantly about the importance of correct breathing. This is because it is of paramount importance to our health. We have many specialised breathing exercises in our Arts. The exercises are designed to help cure many ailments connected to different parts of the body. In the early development of your T'ai Chi, it is important that you allow your breathing to be as natural as possible. Your Instructor will help you to improve your breathing with special breathing exercises.

Special Breathing Techniques are applied to every aspect of the Lee Family Arts.

With correct breathing, a healthy diet and regular practise of all that the LFA Health Arts entail, you can follow the path which the ancient Masters have laid before us.

Taoist Walk

In the LFA we teach the importance of the Taoist Walk, it is included in every book written in this series. The principles of the Taoist Walk apply to all aspects of our health. For example, when the Taoist Walk is harmonised with our specialised breathing exercises and hand movements (which are taught within our classes), it helps to boost the vigour of the immune system. Another exercise, when combined with the Taoist Walk, benefits the heart. We also have specialised movements which while helping to rejuvenate different parts of the body, also provide quite dynamic self defence techniques.

Taoist Walk

The Taoist walk is an extremely important part of the LFA health training because it moves the weight from one leg to another in a special and subtle way.

Not only is one leg working while the other one rests, but the working leg is the Yang leg and the resting leg is the Yin leg.

The weight is moved from one leg to the other before you try and alter the position of your foot.

Start with your feet slightly wider than shoulder width apart, toes pointing forwards.

Both hands are held with the palms facing each other.

9

1/ Drift your weight across to your right side, your right knee bends, your hips and your bottom move across to the right side.

2/ Now take a very small step forwards with your left foot, placing your heel down first. Allow your left knee to bend, move your hips and bottom across to the left. Keep your right leg straight, do not lock your right knee.

Practise walking across the room in this manner. People suffering from back, hip, knee and ankle problems, reap great benefits from practising the Taoist Walk.

We use the Taoist Walk in all of our form sets. With practise it can be incorporated into your every day walk (so that it is undetectable), only you will know the benefits you are receiving each time you place one foot in front of the other.

The Taoist Walk helps to move your Chi energy into the lower part of your body. In the West we tend to carry a lot of energy congestion around the pelvic area, this stagnation leads to the above mentioned problems. So it is a good idea to learn to walk the Taoist Way.

Please try it for yourself, especially if you wake up in the morning feeling stiff, a few minutes practising the Taoist Walk could help to make you feel like a new man or woman.

Etiquette

The etiquette is something which has been handed down through the centuries along with the T'ai Chi. I personally feel it represents a respect for the Arts we are practising and the ancient Masters to whom we owe so much.

When entering or leaving a training hall a student should bow to the room. This bow consists of bending forwards from the waist, at the same time both palms rest on your thighs.

If you arrive after a class has already started you should walk round to the front of the hall, bow to the person taking the class and wait for them to bow to you in return (using the bow explained below).

At the beginning of a class, the bow consists of placing your right arm on top of your left in front of your body, your right palm faces down, and your left palm faces up.

When training with a partner you should both bow to each other at the start and finish of your training (using the same bow as when entering and leaving the training room).

If an instructor offers you guidance with your training, you should bow to them after they have finished teaching you, (again using the bow for entering and leaving the training room).

LFA T'ai Chi Silk Set

The LFA Silk set is a sequence of gentle flowing movements which help you to find the softness and the strength contained within them.

You will find the movements help to improve both your balance and your co-ordination, while at the same time exercising the whole of your body without strain.

It is important to apply the principles of the Taoist Walk to all of your movements (see the section on the Taoist Walk).

To commence your training, you will need a long piece of soft flowing fabric to practise our Silk set (a long scarf is ideal).

People who have already mastered the art of our T'ai Chi Stick will notice certain similarities between the Stick and the Silk sets. The Stick set for example teaches you how to move whilst holding a solid object, whereas the Silk is soft and more fluid in motion.

If you have difficulty with your balance, do not try to stand on one leg, merely rest the ball of your foot on the ground (Cat stance).

All of the different aspects of our Arts are enjoyable and interesting to practise. Initially, you will learn the mechanics i.e. where to place your hands and feet. Next we teach you how to breathe correctly so that you can gain the maximum benefit from the movements.

With time and practise, you will find a hidden depth within the movements which the untrained observer has no idea exists. When you attain this level of understanding, you are truly on your way to attaining good health and an excellent quality of life. However, to reach this level takes many hours of pleasant dedicated practise.

Many people will tell you how practising LFA T'ai Chi has helped to improve the quality of their lives. This is very rewarding to those of us who teach our Arts.

As time passes, people acknowledge that the benefits they thought they had received are only the tip of the iceberg, and that the true benefits of LFA T'ai Chi unfold with the passing of time.

The path is laid before each person who starts to practise LFA T'ai Chi, it is up to each of us as to HOW FAR WE TRAVEL.

LFA T'ai Chi Stances

From the beginning of your training, the LFA emphasise the need for good stances. Stances provide you with your roots. Without correct weight distribution and good balance, you will fall over.

The body should not be held rigidly, nor should it be too laid back, or over relaxed, strive for the middle path. To achieve this takes many hours of pleasant practise.

My late Master described the body as a tree, the legs are the roots and the arms the branches. Each has its own job to do, while at the same time each is separate, yet each is part of the other. This is another example of how Yin and Yang works.

Although you are probably eager to press on and learn the movements of our Silk set. I advise you to take some time to familiarise yourself with the names of our stances and the correct weight distribution for each one.

From the moment you start to practise LFA T'ai Chi you are beginning to use your Chi energy. In the LFA we teach you how to connect valuable energy points within your own body. The LFA do not promise carrots they cannot deliver. We also teach specialised breathing techniques to harness Li energy, otherwise known as 'Macro-Cosmic energy', or the energy of the Universe. Li energy is also referred to as the Yang energy.

Students attending our day courses become more aware of their own Chi energy, sometimes known as the 'Micro - Cosmic energy', or Yin energy, which is the energy within your own body.

The LFA can teach you how to gain control over both energies in order to help you improve the quality of your life.

It is a good idea to practise the stances in front of a mirror, if you attend a regular LFA class your instructor will be able to advise you. For those of you unable to attend classes, take the time to make sure you are comfortable with each posture before you move on to the next.

Bear Stance

Bear stance is achieved by standing with your feet shoulder width apart. Your body should be relaxed with no tension. Both of your arms hang loosely by your sides. Your eyes should be looking straight ahead.

We use Bear stance at the beginning of all our form sets for the 'Prepare' position.

Bee Stance

Bee stance is achieved, by standing with both heels together, and your toes pointing slightly outwards, with both knees bent. Both arms hang loosely by your sides. Your eyes should be looking straight ahead.

Cat Stance

To achieve a Right Cat stance, the left leg is bent at the knee, the heel is raised on your right foot. The ball of the right foot rests lightly on the floor with eighty percent of your weight on your left leg.

To achieve a Left Cat stance, the right leg is bent, the heel is raised on your left foot. The ball of the left foot rests lightly on the floor with eighty percent of your weight on your right leg.

Chicken Stance

To achieve a Right Chicken stance turn ninety degrees to your right. Now place most of your weight onto your right leg (bending the knee). Next bend and lower your left knee towards the floor. This is quite a strong stance, it is important that you listen to your own body and do not strain.

To achieve a Left Chicken stance turn ninety degrees to your left. Now place most of your weight onto your left leg (bending the knee). Next bend and lower your right knee towards the floor. This is quite a strong stance, again it is important that you listen to your own body and do not strain.

CraneStance

To achieve a Right Crane stance, move your weight onto your left leg (bending your left knee slightly to aid your balance). Simultaneously raise your right leg

(bending your right knee) until your right thigh is parallel with the floor. Students who have difficulty balancing should use a Cat stance for movements that require one leg to be lifted off the floor.

To achieve a Left Crane stance take your weight onto your right leg (bending your right knee slightly to aid your balance). At the same time raise your left leg (bending your left knee), your thigh is parallel to the floor.

Crossed Legs Stance

To achieve Right Crossed Legs stance, bend your left knee slightly. Now cross your right leg in front of and slightly beyond your left leg, raise the heel of your right foot.

To achieve Left Crossed Legs stance, bend your right knee slightly. Now cross your left leg in front of and slightly beyond your right leg, raise the heel of your left foot.

Dog Stance

To achieve a Right Dog stance, take your weight onto your left leg (bending the knee slightly to aid your balance). At the same time extend and raise your right leg forwards, your leg should be at a height that is comfortable to you without strain.

To achieve Left Dog stance, take your weight onto your right leg (bending the knee slightly to aid your balance). At the same time extend and raise your left leg forwards.

Dragon Stance

To achieve a Right Dragon stance, step forwards from either a Bear or an Eagle stance. It is important not to over step, make sure you have a good gap (width

ways) between your feet. Drift your weight over to your right side, so that the weight is spread between your right hip, knee and ankle. Eighty percent of your weight should be on your right leg, your left leg should be straight although not locked.

To achieve a Left Dragon stance follow the same procedure as above, this time stepping forwards with your left leg.

27

Duck Stance

To achieve a Right Duck stance from an Eagle stance, step behind with your left foot, placing your heel down first. Now drift your weight onto your left leg

(bending your knee) your right leg should be straight, although not locked.

To achieve a Left Duck stance from an Eagle stance, step back with your right foot, placing your heel down first. Now drift your weight onto your right leg (bending your knee) your left leg should be straight, although not locked.

Eagle Stance

Eagle stance, place both heels together, toes pointing slightly outwards. Your weight should be evenly balanced between both legs.

Hawk Stance

To achieve a Right Hawk stance, move your weight onto your left leg (bending your knee slightly to aid your balance). Next move your right leg out directly behind you (bending your body forward to create a natural line between your leg and your spine). Please remember there should be no strain, listen to your own body.

To achieve a Left Hawk stance, move your weight onto your right leg (bending your knee slightly to aid your balance). Next move your left leg out directly behind you.

Leg Triangle Stance

Your feet should be slightly wider than shoulder width apart, with your weight evenly distributed between both legs. Your arms hang loosely by your sides.

Leopard Stance

To achieve a Right Leopard stance take a pace off sideways to your right (bending your right knee and drifting your weight across). At the same time straighten your left leg. To achieve a Left Leopard stance take a pace off sideways to your left (bending your left knee and drifting your weight across). At the same time straighten your right leg.

Riding Horse

Riding Horse stance, both feet are slightly wider than shoulder width apart (both knees bent) your weight should be evenly distributed between both legs.

Scissors Stance

To achieve a Right Scissors stance, drift your weight onto your left leg (bending your knee slightly). Now cross your right leg behind and slightly beyond your left leg, next raise the heel of your right foot. To achieve a Left Scissors stance, drift your weight onto your right leg (bending your knee slightly). Now cross your left leg behind and slightly beyond your right leg, next raise the heel of your left foot.

Stork Stance

To achieve a Right Stork stance move your weight onto your left leg (bending your left knee slightly to aid your balance). Now raise and bend your right leg moving your foot behind you.

To achieve a Left Stork stance move your weight onto your right leg (bending your right knee slightly to aid your balance). Now raise and bend your left leg moving your foot behind you.

Stances 1 – 156

1	Eagle
2	Eagle
3	Left Dragon
4	Left Cat
5	Left Dragon
6	Right Crane
7	Left Scissors
8	Extended Right Leopard
9	Right Leopard
10	Left Dragon
11	Left Scissors
12	Left Dragon
13	Right Dragon
14	Left Dragon
15	Left Leopard
16	Right Leopard
17	Right Leopard
18	Right Duck
19	Left Cat
20	Left Crane
21	Left Dragon
22	Right Crane
23	Riding Horse
24	Left Cat

25	Left Dragon
26	Left Leopard
27	Left Cat
28	Right Duck
29	Left Leopard
30	Right Leopard
31	Left Stork
32	Left Dragon
33	Right Dragon
34	Left Scissors
35	Extended Right Leopard
36	Right Leopard
37	Left Dragon
38	Right Dragon
39	Left Dragon
40	Left Leopard
41	Right Leopard
42	Right Leopard
43	Right Duck
44	Left Cat
45	Left Crane
46	Left Dragon
47	Left Leopard
48	Right Leopard
49	Left Stork

50	Eagle
51	Right Scissors
52	Left Dragon
53	Right Dragon
54	Right Scissors
55	Left Leopard
56	Left Cat
57	Right Duck
58	Left Crane
59	Left Dragon
60	Right Dragon
61	Right Leopard
62	Left Scissors
63	Right Dragon
64	Left Duck
65	Left Crane
66	Left Dragon
67	Right Duck
68	Right Scissors
69	Bear
70	Left Stork
71	Left Dragon
72	Right Duck
73	Right Cat
74	Right Dragon

75	Left Dragon
76	Left Scissors
77	Right Leopard
78	Left Scissors
79	Right Leopard
80	Left Leopard
81	Right Duck
82	Left Hawk
83	Left Dragon
84	Left Crane
85	Right Crane
86	Right Leopard
87	Right Chicken
88	Left Crane
89	Left Dragon
90	Right Leopard
91	Left Dragon
92	Right Duck
93	Left Duck
94	Right Dragon
95	Right Duck
96	Left Dragon
97	Right Leopard
98	Right Leopard
99	Right Scissors

100	Left Leopard
101	Right Dragon
102	Left Duck
103	Right Duck
104	Riding Horse
105	Left Scissors
106	Left Dragon
107	Left Crane
108	Left Leopard
109	Right Scissors
110	Left Leopard
111	Right Scissors
112	Left Leopard
113	Right Leopard
114	Right Leopard
115	Right Duck
116	Left Duck
117	Right Cat
118	Left Crane
119	Left Hawk
120	Leg Triangle
121	Right Stork
122	Left Stork
123	Right Duck
124	Left Dragon

125	Left Dog
126	Right Duck
127	Right Scissors
128	Left Leopard
129	Right Crossed Legs
130	Right Leopard
131	Left Cat
132	Right Crane
133	Right Hawk
134	Right Leopard
135	Left Dragon
136	Left Scissors
137	Left Dragon
138	Right Dragon
139	Right Leopard
140	Left Leopard
141	Right Leopard
142	Right Leopard
143	Right Crossed Legs
144	Right Dragon
145	Left Duck
146	Right Duck
147	Left Crane
148	Left Crossed Legs
149	Right Dragon

150	Left Dragon
151	Left Dog
152	Left Dragon
153	Left Crane
154	Right Crane
155	Eagle
156	Eagle

The Movements of the LFA T'ai Chi Silk set. Gathering Your Silk

1/Place your right palm face up in front of you, now lay approximately one third of your silk across your palm (the longest part of your silk is furthest away from you).

2/ With your left hand take hold of the longest end of your silk and bring another one third of your silk over the top of your palm (from your right thumb to your right little finger), and place the silk underneath your little finger.

3/ Repeat the procedure once more. Your right hand now rests by your right side, holding your silk.

Prepare

From Eagle stance take a pace off to your left, into prepare (Bear stance), feet shoulder width apart (placing your heel down first), your toes are pointing straight ahead.

At the same time both arms hang loosely by your sides, your right hand still holds your gathered silk by your right side.

Number 1

From Bear stance draw your left leg back to your right leg. Both heels are now touching each other and your toes are pointing slightly outwards, you are now in Eagle stance.

At the same time as you move into Eagle stance, take your left hand across to rest against your right wrist.

Number 2

Remain in Eagle stance for movement number two.
At the same time keep hold of your silk with your
thumb, and let go of the remainder of your silk

which is trapped
underneath your little
finger. Place your left
hand on the silk. Then
raise your right arm
straight up (pulling
the silk through your
left hand) so that the
silk is vertical. Right
hand high – left hand
low. Your eyes look to
the left.

Number 3

From Eagle stance step forwards with your left leg, (placing your heel down first). Remember to keep a gap between your feet (width ways) to ensure good balance. Eighty per cent of your weight should be on your left leg, this is achieve by taking your hip and

bottom across to your left as you bend your left knee, into Left Dragon stance.

At the same time move your left hand forwards and up in a curved motion until it is fully extended at the right hand side of your body. At the same time your right arm circles downwards finishing by your right hip (silk angled upwards from your right hip).

Number 4

From Left Dragon stance transfer your weight onto your right leg by bending your right knee and moving your weight across to the right hand side of your body. Draw your left foot in (flat) then raise your heel. You are now in Left Cat stance.

At the same time circle your silk anti-clockwise, until your left hand is resting by your left hip. Your right arm is fully extended forwards at the left hand side of your body.

Number 5

From Left Cat stance turn ninety degrees to your left by picking up your left foot and placing it into a Left Dragon stance. Remember to put your heel down first, then bend your left knee while at the same time

Lr moving your weight and hips across to the left hand side of your body. Now correct your right foot (heel and toe) turning it forty five degrees to your left.

Rt

At the same time allow your left arm to circle up and your right hand to circle down. Your silk finishes vertical in front of the left hand side of your body (left hand high – right hand low).

Number 6

From Left Dragon Stance, raise and bend your right leg into Right Crane stance (keep your left leg slightly bent to aid your balance). Your right thigh should be parallel to the ground.

Simultaneously circle your right arm forwards then back to finish along side your right ear. At the same time your left hand follows the circle, moving first in a downwards motion then forwards until your left arm is extended at the right hand side of your body.

Number 7

From Right Crane stance place your right foot down on the floor. Pivot on your right heel and turn it ninety degrees to your right. Now place your weight onto your right foot, bend your knees and raise your left heel, you are now in Left Scissors stance.

At the same time, lower both arms, your left arm crosses over the top of your right arm. Look at the right hand side of your silk.

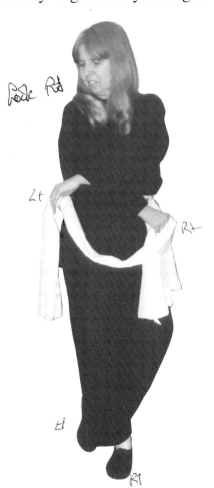

Number 8

From Left Scissors stance place your left heel flat on the floor. Now step sideways to your right into an Extended Right Leopard stance (slightly wider than a normal Leopard stance). Your right leg should be bent

with your weight on the right hand side of your body. Your left leg is straight.

At the same time allow both hands to uncross. Your right arm finishes in front of your right shoulder and your left hand finishes in front of your left hip (your silk is angled downwards from right to left).

Number 9

From Extended Right Leopard simply move to a normal Right Leopard stance. This is achieved by sliding your left foot in towards your right foot (by approximately half a pace). Your hands remain in the same position as they were for movement number 8.

Number 10

From Right Leopard stance turn ninety degrees to your right into Left Dragon stance. This is achieved by moving your weight back onto your left leg, pivoting on the heel of your right foot, and stepping forwards with your left foot into Left Dragon stance.

At the same time allow your right hand to circle underneath your left armpit. Your left arm is extended forwards at shoulder height.

Lf

Rf

Number 11

From Left Dragon stance, step forwards with your right foot (heel down first) and turn your right foot ninety degrees to your right as you step (bend your right knee). Now raise the your left heel, you are now in Left Scissors stance. At the same time, allow your left arm to lower and then cross over your right arm.

Number 12

From Left Scissors stance turn ninety degrees to your left (placing your heel down first) into Left Dragon stance (remember to use the principles of the Taoist Walk).

At the same allow your right arm to circle downwards then over, until it is fully extended forwards in front of your right shoulder. Your left hand circles underneath your right armpit.

Number 13

From Left Dragon stance step forward with your right leg into Right Dragon stance (remember to apply the principles of the Taoist Walk).

At the same time allow your right arm to lower slightly.

Number 14

From Right Dragon stance turn one hundred and eighty degrees to your left into Left Dragon Stance (remember to apply the principles of the Taoist Walk). This movement may take a little practise, it is important to ensure that you are in a good Dragon stance.

At the same time your right arm circles downwards then upwards until it finishes underneath your left armpit. Your left arm circles downwards then upwards to finish extended forwards at shoulder height.

Number 15

From Left Dragon stance turn ninety degrees to the right into Left Leopard stance (remember to apply the principles of the Taoist Walk). Your weight should be at the left hand side of your body (with your knee bent), your right leg is straight.

At the same time allow both arms to circle downwards in an anti-clockwise motion. Your right arm circles past your right shoulder then upwards (see photograph). Your left arm follows the circle finishing at the left hand side of your body (see photograph).

Number 16

From Left Leopard stance keep your feet in the same position, simply transfer your weight across to the right hand side of your body into Right Leopard stance.

At the same time let go of your silk with your left hand (your left hand remains in the same position as it was in for number 15). Keeping hold of your silk in your right hand, circle your right arm outwards and downwards until it finishes extended sideways at shoulder height.

Number 17

Your feet and weight remain in exactly the same position, you are still in Right Leopard stance.

At the same time circle your right hand, making one large full clockwise circle with your silk (your left hand remains in the same position as it was in for movement number 16).

Number 18

From Right Leopard stance turn two hundred and seventy degrees to your left into Right Duck stance. This is achieved with a little jumping movement. Place the right foot down first and bend your left knee (right leg straight, left leg bent).

At the same time your right hand circles up and over the top (towards your left), to finish with your right hand in front of the top of your right thigh (still holding your silk). Your left hand remains in the same position as it was in for movement number 17.

Number 19

From Right Duck stance step through with your left foot into Left Cat stance. The ball of your left foot is resting lightly on the floor, your right knee is bent.
At the same time your right hand remains in the same position as it was in for number 18. Place your left hand on your silk beside your right hand (both thumbs are on the top of the silk).

Number 20

From Left Cat stance raise your left leg, bending your left knee (your thigh should be parallel to the floor). Bend your right knee to help your balance. You are now in Left Crane stance.

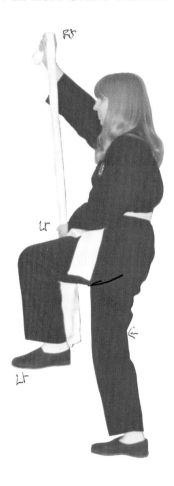

At the same time fully extend your right arm upwards, allow your silk to slide through your left hand (right hand high – left hand low).

Number 21

From Left Crane stance turn one hundred and eighty degrees to your left into Left Dragon stance. Place your left heel down first and bend your left knee. Now move your weight across to the left hand side of

your body. Your right leg is straight but not locked.

At the same time let go of your silk with your right hand. Circle your left arm over the top, until your arm is fully extended forwards.

Number 22

From Left Dragon stance raise your right leg bending your right knee (your thigh should be parallel to the floor). Bend your left knee to help your balance. You are now in Right Crane stance.

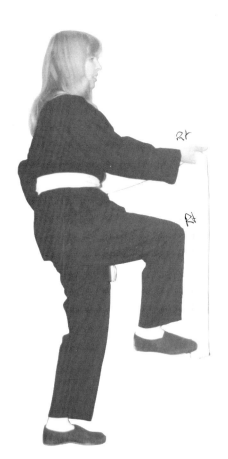

At the same time catch hold of your silk with your right hand (palm facing up). Lower your left arm so that your left wrist is against your waist, your silk slides over your right palm.

Number 23

From Right Crane stance turn ninety degrees to your right into Riding Horse. This is achieved by placing your right foot down then correcting your left foot (heel and toe), bend both knees and sink your weight. At the same time change your right hand from palm up to palm down. Circle your silk to the right above your head then to your left so that your silk rests along the back of your neck and left arm, (left arm fully extended sideways at shoulder height, fingertips drooped). Your right hand is touching your right shoulder.

Number 24

From Riding horse stance turn ninety degrees to your right into Left Cat stance. Pivot on the heel of your right foot and bend your right knee slightly. Now raise the heel of your left foot.

At the same time let go of your silk with your left hand and allow the free end of your silk to fall. Your right hand remains on your right shoulder, and your left hand moves to join it. (Both hands are holding the silk).

Number 25

From Left Cat stance step through into Left Dragon stance placing your left heel down first. Bend your left knee and move your weight across to the left hand

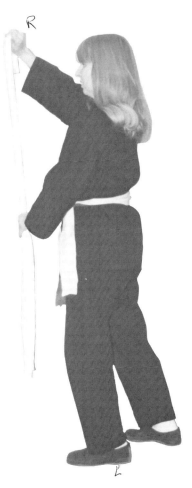

side of your body. Your right leg is straight, although the knee is relaxed.

At the same time let go of your silk with your left hand. Circle your right arm down behind you then forwards in an upwards motion, (right arm extended upwards). Catch hold of your silk with your left hand (your left hand is at waist height, in front of you).

Number 26

From Left Dragon stance turn ninety degrees to your right into Left Leopard stance. This is achieved by moving the heel and toe of your left foot and then

moving your right foot. Bend your left knee, moving your weight across to the left hand side of your body.

At the same time your right arm sweeps out to the right then circles back, to stop in front of and above, the right side of your head. Your silk is angled down to the left.

Number 27

From Left Leopard stance turn ninety degrees to your right into Left Cat stance. Lift the heel of your left foot, your right knee is slightly bent.

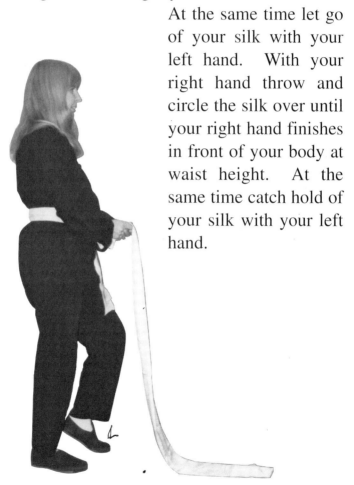

At the same time let go of your silk with your left hand. With your right hand throw and circle the silk over until your right hand finishes in front of your body at waist height. At the same time catch hold of your silk with your left hand.

Number 28

From Left Cat stance step back with your left foot (placing your left heel down first) into Right Duck stance. Bend your left knee and move your weight across to the left hand side of your body. Your right leg is straight (foot flat).

At the same time pull your silk over your right hand. Bend your left elbow and bring it to rest by your waist. Your right arm is extended forwards.

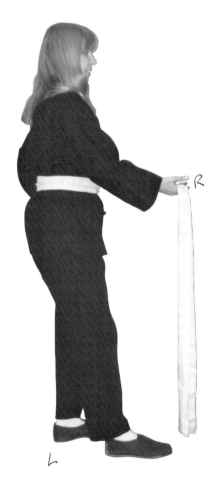

Number 29

From Right Duck stance turn your right foot ninety degrees to your right. Step through with your left leg, into Left Leopard stance. Bend your left knee and move your weight across to the left hand side of your body.

At the same time change the position of your right hand to palm down. Now circle your silk downwards then upwards in an anticlockwise movement until your right hand is approximately at head height (right hand side). Your left hand is at shoulder height (left hand side).

Number 30

From Left Leopard stance, adjust your weight across into a Right Leopard stance (do not move your feet). To achieve this, bend your right knee, straighten your left knee while moving your weight across to the right hand side of your body.

At the same time lower your right hand so that your silk is horizontal.

Number 31

From Right Leopard stance keep your weight on your right leg. Now raise and bend your left knee, your foot is slightly behind you (toes pointing downwards). You are now in Left Stork stance.

At the same time let go of your silk with your left hand. With your right hand circle your silk in an anti clockwise direction (over your head, behind your body and back to the front). Your right hand extends upwards holding your silk. Your left hand takes hold of your silk, at the end of the movement.

Number 32

From Left Stork stance step forwards with your left foot into Left Dragon stance. Remembering to apply the Taoist Walk.

At the same time allow your left hand to circle forwards and your right hand to circle downwards finishing along side your right hip.

Number 33

From Left Dragon stance turn ninety degrees to your right into Right Dragon stance. This is achieved by picking up your right foot and placing it into position (heel down first). Next, bend your right knee and move your weight across to your right hand side.

Correct your left foot, heel and toe. At the same time circle your right arm forwards until it is fully extended, then over, until it circles back to your right hip. Your left arm circles back towards your left hip, then forwards to finish in the same position as it started from, (although facing ninety degrees to the right).

Number 34

From Right Dragon stance turn the toes of your right foot ninety degrees to your right and simultaneously raise the heel of your left foot. Both legs should now be crossed. You are now in Left Scissors stance. Your body should have also turned ninety degrees with the turn of your feet.

At the same time allow your left elbow to bend and cross your left arm over your right.

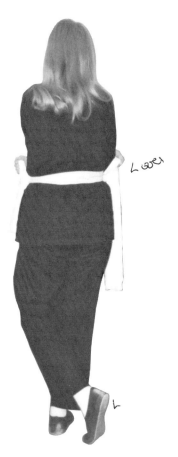

Number 35

From Left Scissors stance place your left heel flat on the floor. Step off to your right with your right foot so that your feet are slightly wider than shoulder width apart. Bend your right knee a little deeper than normal (if this is possible without strain). Move your weight across to the right hand side of your body, you are now in Extended Right Leopard stance.

At the same time allow your arms to uncross. Your left arm moves in front of your left hip, your right arm moves up in front of your right shoulder.

Number 36

From Extended Right Leopard stance simply draw your left foot in towards your right foot (half a pace) into Right Leopard stance.

Both hands remain in exactly the same position as they were in for movement number 35.

Number 37

From Right Leopard stance turn ninety degrees to your right into Left Dragon stance. Move your weight across to your left side, pivot on the heel of your right foot and step through with your left leg into Left Dragon stance.

At the same time allow your left arm to circle up and over until it is extended forwards in front of your left shoulder. Your right hand circles downwards to finish underneath your left armpit.

Number 38

From Left Dragon stance step forwards into Right Dragon stance, using the Taoist Walk.

At the same time allow your left arm to lower slightly.

Number 39

From Right Dragon stance turn one hundred and eighty degrees to your left into Left Dragon stance. Remember to use the Taoist Walk.

At the same time allow both arms to sweep down and up with the turn of your body, finishing with your left arm extended forwards and your right hand underneath your left armpit.

Number 40

From Left Dragon stance turn ninety degrees to your right into Left Leopard stance, using the Taoist Walk. Your weight finishes at your left hand side with your left knee bent and your right leg straight.

At the same time circle your silk out to the right to finish in front of you, (angled down from right to left).

Number 41

From Left Leopard stance transfer your weight across to your right side into Right Leopard stance (do not move your feet).

At the same time let go of your silk with your left hand (your left hand remains in the same extended position). Your right hand moves out to the right (extended at shoulder height with the silk hanging down).

Number 42

Remain in Right Leopard stance.
At the same time make a large clockwise circle with your silk in front of your body. Finishing in the same position as you were in for movement number 41.

Number 43

From Right Leopard stance turn two hundred and seventy degrees to your left into Right Duck stance. Your weight should be on the left hand side of your body, with your left knee bent. Your right leg is straight.

At the same time your right hand moves over and down to finish extended in front of your body. The free end of your silk rests on the floor in front of you. Your left hand remains in the same position as it was in for movement number 42.

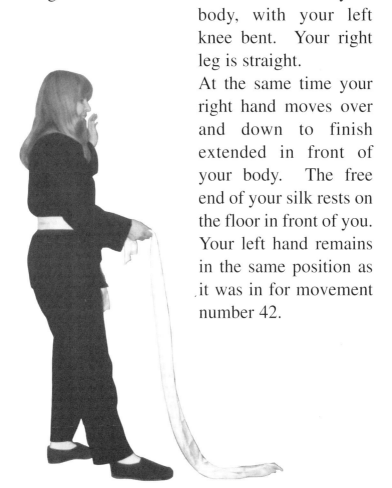

Number 44

From Right Duck stance, step through with your left foot and raise your left heel into Left Cat stance.

At the same time lower your left hand to waist height so that you are holding your silk with both hands (thumbs on the top).

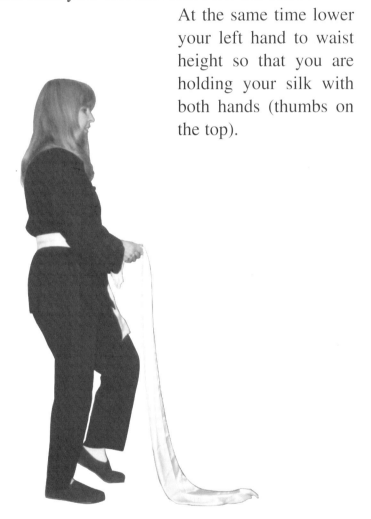

Number 45

From Left Cat stance, raise and bend your left knee (thigh parallel to the floor). You are now in Left Crane stance. Bend your right knee slightly to help your balance.

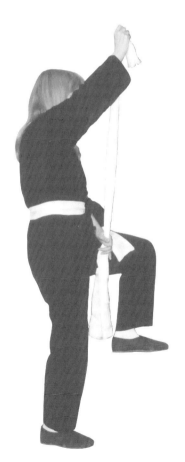

At the same time, raise your right elbow and pull your silk through your left hand until your silk is vertical in front of your body.

Number 46

From Left Crane stance, step through into Left Dragon stance. Remember to use the Taoist Walk.

At the same time allow your left hand to circle forwards and up. Your right hand circles downwards, finishing by your right hip (silk angled upwards from your right hip).

Number 47

From Left Dragon stance turn ninety degrees to your right into Left Leopard stance. Remember to use the Taoist Walk.

At the same time allow both arms to circle to the right finishing with your silk in front of you angled downwards from right to left (see photograph).

Number 48

From Left Leopard stance transfer your weight into Right Leopard stance (your feet do not move).
At the same time lower your right arm until the silk is horizontal.

Number 49

From Right Leopard stance raise and bend your left knee so that your foot is behind you with your toes pointing to the ground. You are now in Left Stork stance.

At the same time let go of your silk with your left hand. With your right hand, circle your silk around the back of your head, to finish with it hanging over your right shoulder.

Number 50

From Left Stork stance place your left foot beside your right foot, you are now in Eagle stance (toes pointing slightly outwards).

At the same time simply gather your silk in your right hand (i.e. As in the starting position).

Number 51

From Eagle stance, cross your right leg behind your left leg into Right Scissors stance (both knees slightly bent, your right heel is raised).

At the same time let go of the silk with your left hand and circle your right hand forwards and over. Next catch the free end of your silk with your left hand. Your right hand is high and your left hand is low (see photograph).

Number 52

From Right Scissors stance turn ninety degrees to your left into Left Dragon stance. Remember to use the Taoist Walk.

At the same time your left arm extends upwards. Your right hand moves across to the left hand side of your body (see photograph).

Number 53

From Left Dragon stance, step through into Right Dragon stance. Remember to use the Taoist Walk.
At the same time let go of your silk with your left

hand. Circle your right hand forwards and over, then catch the free end of your silk with your left hand. Your right arm finishes extended forwards at shoulder height, your left hand finishes by your left hip.

Number 54

From Right Dragon stance turn your left foot ninety degrees to your left (place your weight onto your left foot) now cross your right leg behind your left and raise your right heel. You are now in Right Scissors stance.

At the same time, cross your left arm over your right arm.

Number 55

From Right Scissors stance, place your right heel flat on the floor and step sideways with your left foot into Left Leopard stance. Your left knee should be bent and your right leg should be straight.

At the same move your left hand up to your left shoulder and your right hand down to your right hip.

Number 56

From Left Leopard stance turn ninety degrees to your right into Left Cat stance. Your left heel is raised and your right leg is slightly bent.

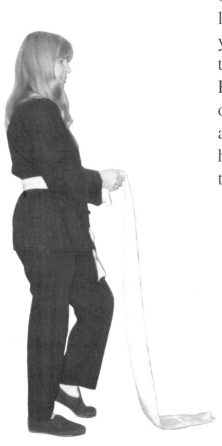

At the same time let go of your silk with your left hand as you swing your silk over with the turn of your body. Replace your left hand on the end of your silk, along side your right hand (both thumbs on the top).

Number 57

From Left Cat stance, step behind with your left foot into Right Duck stance. Place your left heel down first, transfer your weight onto your left leg and straighten your right leg.

At the same time pull the silk through your right hand with your left hand. Your left hand finishes by your left hip (right hand palm up).

Number 58

From Right Duck stance, raise your left leg into Left Crane stance. Your left thigh should be parallel to the floor, bend your right knee slightly to help your balance.

At the same time let go of your silk with your right hand, then transfer the silk from your left hand to your right hand. Now circle your silk slightly to the right then underneath your left leg, catching the free end of your silk with your left hand.

Number 59

From Left Crane stance, step forwards into Left Dragon stance. Remember to use the Taoist Walk.

At the same time let go of your silk with your left

hand, swing the silk over your right shoulder with your left hand. Now place your left hand alongside your right hand on your right shoulder. Both hands are now holding the silk.

Number 60

From Left Dragon stance, step through into Right Dragon stance. Remember to use the Taoist Walk.

At the same time let go of your silk with your left hand, circle your right arm slightly behind then forwards. Catch hold of the free end of your silk with your left hand, then draw your left hand back to your left hip.

Number 61

From Right Dragon stance turn ninety degrees to the right into Right Leopard stance. Your right knee is bent and your left leg is straight.

At the same time let go of the silk with your left hand, circle the silk forwards and over with your right hand, then catch the free end with your left hand (pulling the silk through your left hand). The silk finishes angled downwards from your right shoulder to your left hip.

Number 62

From Right Leopard stance cross your left leg behind your right into Left Scissors stance. Both knees are slightly bent, the heel is raised on your left foot.
At the same time cross your left hand over your right arm.

Number 63

From Left Scissors stance, turn ninety degrees to your right into Right Dragon stance. Remember to use the Taoist Walk.

At the same time let go of your silk with your left hand, circle your silk over to the right (as you turn your body to the right). Catch the free end of your silk with your left hand (pulling the silk through your left hand). Your left hand finishes near your left hip and your right hand extends forward at shoulder height.

Number 64

From Right Dragon stance, step backwards with your right foot into Left Duck stance. Place your right heel down first and transfer the weight onto your right leg and straighten your left leg.

At the same time circle your right hand down to your right hip, your left hand extends forwards at shoulder height.

Number 65

From Left Duck stance, raise your left leg into Left Crane stance. Your left thigh should be parallel to the floor, bend your right knee slightly to help your balance.

At the same time let go of your silk with your left hand and circle your silk to the right and then underneath your left leg. Catch the free end of your silk with your left hand.

Number 66

From left Crane stance, turn one hundred and eighty degrees to your left into Left Dragon stance. Remember to use the Taoist Walk.

At the same time let go of the silk with your right hand and circle your silk over, to finish at waist height on the left hand side of your body.

Number 67

From Left Dragon stance, step back into Right Duck stance. Place your left heel down first, transfer the weight onto your left leg and straighten your right leg.

At the same time turn your right palm upwards and pull your silk over your right palm. Your left hand finishes by your left hip.

Number 68

From Right Duck stance, turn ninety degrees to your left into Right Scissors stance. Take your weight slightly forwards onto your right foot to allow you to turn your left foot, then transfer your weight back

onto your left foot as you turn your body and cross your right foot behind your left foot, now raise your right heel.

At the same time, let go of the silk with your right hand and then transfer the silk from your left hand to your right hand. Now circle your silk forward to your right as you make your turn. Catch your silk in your left hand, and pull it through your left hand (the silk finishes angled down from your right shoulder to your left hip).

Number 69

From Right Scissors stance, turn one hundred and eighty degrees to your right into Bear stance (feet shoulder width apart, legs straight).

At the same time your silk moves round with the turn of your body to finish horizontal in front of your shoulders.

Number 70

From Bear stance raise and bend your left leg, moving
· it behind you with your toes pointing downwards. You
are now in Left Stork stance.

At the same time let go
of your silk with your
left hand, circling it
around your body to
finish vertical (down
the centre line of your
body). Right hand high
– left hand low.

Number 71

From Left Stork stance turn ninety degrees to your left into Left Dragon stance. Remember to use the Taoist Walk.

At the same time let go of your silk with your right hand and circle (flip) your silk over, catching it with your right hand and drawing your right hand back to your right hip. Your silk finishes angled upwards from your right hip.

Number 72

From Left Dragon stance, step behind with your left foot (placing the heel down first) into Right Duck stance (left leg bent, right leg straight).

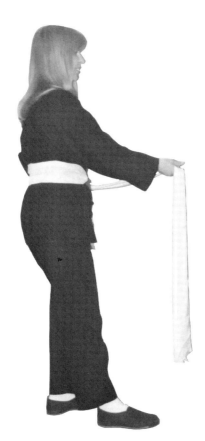

At the same time let go of the silk with your right hand. Turn your right hand palm up and move it across to the centre of your body. Now pull the silk through your right hand until your left hand reaches your left hip.

Number 73

From Right Duck stance, turn one hundred and eighty degrees to your left into Right Cat stance. This is achieved by pivoting on the heel of your left foot.

At the same time let go of your silk with your right hand, circling your silk over with the turn of your body. Replace your right hand on the silk. (See photograph).

Number 74

From Right Cat stance, step through into Right Dragon stance. Remember to use the Taoist Walk. Let go of your silk with your left hand and circle it over with your right hand. Now catch the silk with your left hand. The silk finishes angled upwards from your left hip.

Number 75

From Right Dragon stance, step through into Left Dragon stance. Remember to use the Taoist Walk.

At the same time let go of your silk with your right hand, circle your silk forwards and over with your left hand. Catch the silk with your right hand, your silk finishes angled upwards from your right hip.

Number 76

From Left Dragon stance turn ninety degrees to your right into Left Scissors stance. First turn your right foot then cross your left leg behind it (raise the heel of your left foot).

At the same time your left arm crosses over your right arm.

Number 77

From Left Scissors stance place your left heel down and step sideways into Right Leopard stance. Transfer your weight across to your right side and straighten your left leg.

At the same time move your right hand to your right shoulder and your left hand to your left hip.

Number 78

From Right Leopard stance turn one hundred and eighty degrees to the right into Left Scissors stance. First move your weight across to the left to enable you

to move your right foot, then raise the heel of your left foot as your legs cross.

At the same time your left arm crosses over your right arm.

Number 79

From Left Scissors stance place your left heel down and step sideways with your right foot into Right Leopard stance. Transfer your weight across to your right side bending your right knee, then straighten your left leg. At the same time your right hand moves to your right shoulder and your left hand moves to your left hip.

Number 80

From Right Leopard stance turn one hundred and eighty degrees to your right into Left Leopard stance. Remember to use the Taoist Walk. First move your weight onto your left leg, pivot on your right heel, then move your weight onto your left leg.

At the same time move your left hand to your left shoulder and your right hand to your right hip.

Number 81

From Left Leopard stance turn ninety degrees to your left into Right Duck stance. This is achieved by pivoting on the heel of your right foot, then stepping behind with your left foot (placing the heel down first).

At the same time glide your left hand down to your left hip and your right hand up to your right shoulder.

Number 82

From Right Duck stance swing your left leg behind into Left Hawk stance. Bend your right leg to help your balance.

At the same time let go of your silk with your left hand and circle your silk over, catching it with your left hand by your left hip. Your silk finishes extended forward from your left hip (see photograph).

Number 83

From Left Hawk stance, step through into Left Dragon stance. Remember to use the Taoist Walk.

At the same time let go of your silk with your left

hand, circle your right hand and silk around your back. Exchange your right hand for your left hand, now move your silk to the front of your body replacing your right hand on the silk. Your silk finishes vertical in front of the left hand side of your body. Left hand high – right hand low.

Number 84

From Left Dragon stance, raise and bend your left leg into Left Crane stance (thigh parallel to the ground. Bend your right leg to help your balance.

At the same time let go of your silk with your left hand and circle it underneath your left leg, catching it with your left hand.

Number 85

From Left Crane stance, place your left foot down on the floor and raise your right leg into Right Crane stance (thigh parallel to the ground). Bend your left

leg to help your balance. At the same time let go of your silk with your right hand, circle your left hand over to meet your right hand, now place the silk in your right hand and let go of it with your left hand. Circle your right hand underneath your right leg and catch the free end of your silk with your left hand.

Number 86

From Right Crane stance, step sideways with your right foot into Right Leopard stance (placing your heel down first). Right leg bent, left leg straight.

At the same time let go of your silk with your right hand, pull your silk through with your left hand. Now exchange your left hand for your right hand, then replace your left hand back on the silk. Slide your left hand down the silk to your left hip. Your silk finishes on the diagonal from your right shoulder to your left hip (see photgraph).

Number 87

From Right Leopard stance, turn ninety degrees to your right into Right Chicken stance. Your right leg is in front of your left, with your knee bent. Your left leg is behind you with your knee bent (nearly touching the floor).

At the same time let go of your silk with your left hand circling it over with the turn of your body. Now replace your left hand next to your right hand on the silk, (thumbs on the top).

Number 88

From Right Chicken stance, raise yourself up into Left Crane stance (thigh parallel to the floor). Bend your right leg to help your balance.

At the same time pull the silk up through your left hand, until it finishes inside your left thigh (right hand high – left hand low).

Number 89

From Left Crane stance, turn ninety degrees to your left into Left Dragon stance. Remember to use the Taoist Walk.

At the same time circle your right hand down to your right hip and extend your left hand forwards. Your silk finishes on the diagonal extended forwards from your left shoulder down to your right hip.

Number 90

From Left Dragon stance, turn ninety degrees to the left into Right Leopard stance (using the Taoist Walk). At the same time let go of your silk with your left hand, (flip) your silk as you circle your right arm over. Catch the free end of your silk with your left hand. Your silk finishes on the diagonal across your body (right hand high – left hand low).

Number 91

From Right Leopard stance, turn ninety degrees to your left into Left Dragon stance. Remember to use the Taoist Walk.

At the same time both arms sweep down and up to finish in front of the centre line of your body (left hand high – right hand low).

Number 92

From Left Dragon stance, step behind with your left foot into Right Duck stance (placing your left heel down first). Left leg bent, right leg straight.

At the same time your left hand circles back to finish on your left shoulder (palm up). Your right arm is extended forwards (see photograph).

Number 93

From Right Duck stance, pivot on your right heel ninety degrees to your right, then step with your left foot into Right Duck stance, then step behind with your right foot into Left Duck stance (placing your right heel down first). Right leg bent, left leg straight.

At the same time, circle your right hand back to your right shoulder (palm up). Your left arm is extended forwards.

Number 94

From Left Duck stance, turn one hundred and eighty degrees to the right into Right Dragon stance. Remember to use the Taoist Walk.

At the same time let go of your silk with your left hand and circle your right hand over with the turn of your body. The silk is held in your right hand, your left hand is by your left side.

Number 95

From Right Dragon stance, transfer your weight into Right Duck stance. Left leg bent, right leg straight.

At the same time take hold of the silk with your left hand and draw the silk over your right hand, until your left hand is by your left hip. (See photograph for movement number 28).

Number 96

From Right Duck stance, step forwards into Left Dragon stance. Remember to use the Taoist Walk.
At the same time let go of your silk with your right

hand, now exchange the silk from your left hand to your right hand. Circle your right hand over (flip), and catch the free end of your silk in your left hand. The silk finishes on the diagonal (right hand high at your right shoulder – left hand low at your left hip).

Number 97

From Left Dragon stance, turn ninety degrees to your right into Right Leopard stance. Place your right foot in position, then your left. Right leg bent, left leg straight.

At the same time let go of your silk with your left hand, circle (flip) your silk over with your right hand as you turn. Catch the free end of your silk with your left hand. Your silk finishes angled downwards across your body from right to left.

Number 98

From Right Leopard stance, turn one hundred and eighty degrees to your right into Right Leopard stance.

Your silk remains in the same position.

Number 99

From Right Leopard stance, take your right leg behind your left leg into Right Scissors stance. This is achieved by bending both knees and raising your right heel.

At the same time leg go of your silk with your left hand and circle your right hand over. The movement finishes with your silk in the same position as it was in for the previous movement.

Number 100

From Right Scissors stance, place your heel down first and step sideways with your left foot into Left Leopard stance. Left leg bent, right leg straight.
At the same time raise your left hand to shoulder height and lower your right hand to your right hip (see photograph).

Number 101

From Left Leopard stance turn ninety degrees to your right into Right Dragon stance. Remember to use the Taoist Walk.

At the same time your right hand sweeps forwards and up to extend at shoulder height.   Your left hand sweeps down towards your left hip on the diagonal.

Number 102

From Right Dragon stance, step behind with your right leg into Left Duck stance (placing your right heel down first). Right leg bent, left leg straight.

At the same time your right hand sweeps down to your right hip and your left hand sweeps up to extend forwards at shoulder height.

Number 103

From Left Duck stance step behind with your left foot into Right Duck stance (placing your left heel down first). Left leg bent, right leg straight.

At the same time your left hand sweeps down towards your left hip and your right hand sweeps up to extend forwards at shoulder height.

Number 104

From Right Duck stance, turn ninety degrees to your right into Riding Horse stance.
At the same time lower your right hand so that your silk finishes horizontal at waist height.

Number 105

From Riding Horse stance, turn one hundred and eighty degrees to your right into Left Scissors stance. Your silk remains in the same position.

Number 106

From Left Scissors stance turn ninety degrees to your left into Left Dragon stance.

At the same time circle your right hand onto your right shoulder (palm up), and extend your left arm forwards at shoulder height.

Number 107

From Left Dragon stance, raise your leg up into Left Crane stance.

Your silk remains in the same position as it was in for movement number 106.

Number 108

From Left Crane stance, turn ninety degrees to the left into Left Leopard stance.

At the same time allow your right hand to move down to your right hip and your left hand to move up to your left shoulder.

Number 109

From Left Leopard stance, step behind with your right leg into Right Scissors stance.

At the same time allow your left arm to cross over your right.

Number 110

From Right Scissors stance, step sideways with your left foot into Left Leopard stance.

At the same time allow both arms to unfold. Your left hand is near your left shoulder and your right hand is near your right hip.

Number 111

From Left Leopard stance, move your right leg behind into Right Scissors stance.

At the same time allow your left arm to cross over your right arm.

Number 112

From Right Scissors stance, step sideways into Left Leopard stance.

At the same time allow both arms to unfold. Your left hand is near your left shoulder and your right hand is near your right hip.

Number 113

From Left Leopard stance, transfer your weight across into Right Leopard stance.

At the same time let go of your silk with your left hand (move your left hand up to shoulder height, see photograph). Your right hand, circles your silk over to your right side (like movement number 16).

Number 114

Stay in Right Leopard stance.
At the same time complete one large clockwise circle
with your silk (like movement number 17).

Number 115

From Right Leopard stance turn two hundred and seventy degrees to the left into Right Duck stance.

At the same time your right arm circles over as you make your turn. Your silk finishes extended forwards on the floor in front of you. Your left arm is still in the same position it was in for movement number 114.

Number 116

From Right Duck stance, step behind with your right foot into Left Duck stance.

At the same time replace your left hand on the silk then raise and draw your right hand back to your right ear. Your left arm is extended forwards at the right hand side of your body (shoulder height).

Number 117

From Left Duck stance, turn one hundred and eighty degrees to the right into Right Cat stance.

At the same time let go of your silk with your left hand. Circle your right hand over with the turn of your body. Replace your left hand on your silk, (next to your right hand at waist height, with your thumbs on the top).

Number 118

From Right Cat stance, place your right heel down and raise your left leg into Left Crane stance.

Move your right hand towards your right ear, pulling the silk through your left hand.

At the same time your left hand extends forwards in front of your right shoulder.

Number 119

From Left Crane stance, extend your left leg to the rear into Left Hawk stance.

At the same time your right hand circles underneath your left armpit. Your left arm is extended forwards at shoulder height.

Number 120

From Left Hawk stance, swing your left leg slightly forwards then down into Leg Triangle.

At the same time bring both hands together in front of the chest (prayer position). NOTE:-the photograph shows the front view, but the actual stance is with the back facing to the camera.

Number 121

From Leg Triangle stance, raise and bend your right leg, moving it behind you with your toes pointing downwards. You are now in Right Stork stance.

At the same time point both hands downwards (palms together). NOTE:-the photograph shows the front view, but the actual stance is with the back facing to the camera.

Number 122

From Right Stork stance, turn one hundred and eighty degrees to your right into Left Stork stance.

At the same time let go of your silk with your left hand. Your right hand circles over with the turn of your body. Replace your left hand alongside your right hand. Both hands finish at waist height, the free end of your silk should be on the floor in front of your left foot.

Number 123

From Left Stork stance, step behind into Right Duck stance.

At the same time circle your right arm behind your

back, now exchange your right hand for your left. Continue to circle the silk to the front of your body with your left hand. Replace your right hand back on to the silk. Next pull the silk through your right hand. Your silk finishes vertical down the centre line of your body (left hand high – right hand low).

169

Number 124

From Right Duck stance, turn one hundred and eighty degrees to your left into Left Dragon stance (remember to use your Taoist Walk).

At the same time your left hand circles underneath your right arm pit. Your right arm is extended forwards at shoulder height.

Number 125

From Left Dragon stance swing your left leg up into Left Dog stance.

At the same time circle your right hand back to your right shoulder (palm up) and your left hand forward (see photograph).

Number 126

From Left Dog stance, step behind with your left leg into Right Duck stance.

At the same time circle your left hand back to your left shoulder and your right arm forward (see photograph).

Number 127

From Right Duck stance, turn ninety degrees to the left into Right Scissors stance.

At the same time cross both arms, your right arm is underneath your left arm.

Number 128

From Right Scissors stance, step sideways with your left foot into Left Leopard stance.

At the same time uncross your arms so that your silk finishes angled on the diagonal, (left hand high at the left shoulder – right hand low at the right hip).

Number 129

From Left Leopard stance, cross your right leg in front of your left leg into Right Crossed legs stance (both knees are slightly bent and your right heel is raised). At the same time cross your right arm, over your left arm.

Number 130

From Right Crossed legs stance, step sideways with your right foot into Right Leopard stance.

At the same time uncross your arms so that your silk finishes on the diagonal across the front of your body (right hand high at your right shoulder – left hand low at your left hip).

Number 131

From Right Leopard stance turn ninety degrees to your right into Left Cat stance.

At the same time let go of your silk with your left hand. Circle your right arm over with the turn of your body. Now replace your left hand on your silk next to your right hand. Your silk finishes at waist height, with the free end of your silk on the floor in front of your feet. (See photograph for movement number 19).

Number 132

From Left Cat stance, raise your right leg into Right Crane stance (right knee bent, thigh parallel to the floor).

At the same raise your right hand and draw the silk up through your left hand.

Number 133

From Right Crane stance, and extend your right leg out behind you into Right Hawk stance.
At the same time your left hand circles underneath your right armpit.

Number 134

From Right Hawk stance, turn ninety degrees to your right into Right Leopard stance.

At the same time circle your right hand back to your right shoulder, and your left hand back to your left hip.

Number 135

From Right Leopard stance turn ninety degrees to your right into Left Dragon stance.

At the same time circle your right hand underneath your left armpit.

Number 136

From Left Dragon stance, step through with your right foot into Left Scissors stance turning your body ninety degrees to your right (like number 11). At the same time your left arm crosses over your right (also like movement number 11).

Number 137

From Left Scissors stance step through with your left leg into Left Dragon stance (like movement number 12).

At the same time uncross your left arm circling it underneath your right arm pit (also like movement number 12).

Number 138

From Left Dragon stance step through into Right Dragon stance (like movement number 13).

At the same time simply lower your right arm slightly (like movement number 13).

Number 139

From Right Dragon stance, turn ninety degrees to your right (stepping back with your right foot) into Right Leopard stance.

At the same time let go of your silk with your left hand, circle your silk over to the right and catch the silk with your left hand. Your silk finishes on the diagonal (right hand high – left hand low).

Number 140

From Right Leopard stance, keep your feet in the same position and move your weight across into Left Leopard stance.

At the same time raise your left hand up to your left shoulder and lower your right hand down to your right hip (see photograph).

Number 141

From Left Leopard stance, keep your feet in the same position and move your weight across into Right Leopard stance.

At the same time let go of your silk with your left hand (keep your left hand in the same position).
Extend your arm out sideways (like movement number 16).

Number 142

Stay in Right Leopard stance for number one hundred and fortytwo.

At the same time, your right arm completes a large clockwise circle with your silk.

Number 143

From Right Leopard stance cross your right leg in front of your left leg into Right Crossed Legs stance.

At the same time exchange your silk from your right hand to your left hand. Now turn your right palm upwards and draw the silk across your right hand. Your silk finishes horizontal at head height.

Number 144

From Right Crossed Legs stance, turn ninety degrees to your right into Right Dragon stance.

At the same time let go of your silk with your left hand. Now circle (flip) your silk with your right hand. Catch the free end of your silk with your left hand, your silk finishes angled down from your right shoulder to your left hip (see photograph).

Number 145

From Right Dragon stance, step behind with your right leg into Left Duck stance.

At the same time move your right hand down to your right hip, your left hand is extended forwards at shoulder height. Your silk finishes angled down to your right hip (see photograph).

Number 146

From Left Duck stance step behind with your left leg into Right Duck stance.

At the same time move your left hand to your left hip, your right hand extends forwards at shoulder height.

Number 147

From Right Duck stance turn ninety degrees to the right into Left Crane stance.

At the same time let go of your silk with your left hand. Circle your right arm out to the right then back so that the free end of your silk moves underneath your left leg. Now catch the free end of your silk with your left hand (see photograph).

Number 148

From Left Crane stance, cross your left leg in front of your right leg into Left Crossed Legs stance.

At the same time let go of your silk with your right hand. Now exchange the silk from your left hand to your right hand. Replace your left hand on the free end of your silk. Your silk finishes on the diagonal, across your body (right hand high – left hand low).

Number149

From Left Crossed Legs stance, turn ninety degrees to your right into Right Dragon stance.

At the same time let go of your silk with your left hand, circle your right hand over as you (flip your silk forwards) and turn your body to the right. Now catch the free end of your silk with your left hand. Your silk now finishes angled upwards from your left hip on the left hand side of your body.

Number 150

From Right Dragon stance, turn one hundred and eighty degrees to your left into Left Dragon stance. At the same time your left hand circles underneath your right armpit.

Number 151

From Left Dragon stance, swing your left leg up into Left Dog stance.

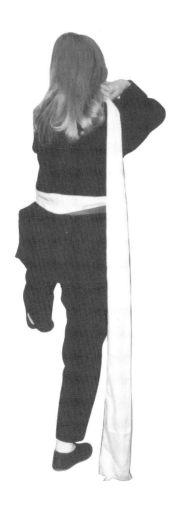

At the same time let go of your silk with your left hand and swing your silk over your right shoulder. Then replace your left hand on the silk, next to your right hand.

Number 152

From Left Dog stance, step through into Left Dragon stance.

At the same time let go of your silk with your left hand. Circle your right hand behind you and then around to the front, sweeping the free end forwards and upwards. Catch the free end with your left hand. The silk slides through your left hand by the pulling action of your right hand. Your right hand finishes by your right hip and your left hand is extended forwards at the right hand side of your body.

Number 153

From Left Dragon stance, turn ninety degrees to your right into Left Crane stance.

At the same time raise your right arm up so that your silk finishes inside your left thigh (right hand high – left hand low).

Number 154

From Left Crane stance, place your left foot down on the floor and raise your right leg into Right Crane stance.

At the same time your right hand circles downwards and your left hand moves upwards with the silk vertical inside your right thigh.

Number 155

From Right Crane stance, turn ninety degrees to your right placing your right foot flat on the floor into Eagle stance.

At the same time place both hands together in the prayer position.

Number 156

Remain in Eagle stance for movement one hundred and fifty six.
Fold both arms and bow.

Now you have completed all one hundred and fiftysix movements of our T'ai Chi Silk set, you are ready to move to a deeper level of understanding. This will take time and practise.

I will be here to help you every step of the way, through my classes, day courses, summer schools, videos and books. Please remember our Silk set provides only one branch of the tree. To reap the full benefit of our Arts you need to learn every aspect of them.

I hope you continue to enjoy your journey with the LFA T'ai Chi.

Best Regards
Sheila Dickinson
LFA President

THE LFA T'AI CHI LIBRARY

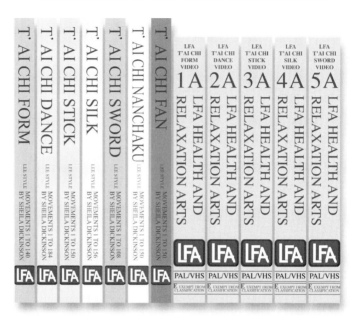

All of the above Books and Videos are available from:-
Stairway Distribution Limited
PO Box 19
Hedon
HU12 8YR
Tel/Fax 01482 896063

You may also order from our Website catalogue, please visit
www.leefamilyarts.com

LFA T' AI CHI SILK

Notes

LFA T'AI CHI SILK

Notes